CW00863711

Written by Odile Limousin
Illustrated by Laura Bour

Specialist advisers:
S. J. Cackett, Department of Physical Sciences,
The Science Museum, London
P. J. Doyle, British Glass, Sheffield

ISBN: 1 85103 068 9
First published 1989 in the United Kingdom by
Moonlight Publishing Ltd
36 Stratford Road, London W8
Translated by Sarah Gibson

POCKET • WORLDS

What is Glass?

Look out of the window . . .

Be careful – it's made of glass! Bottles, jars, tumblers, wine-glasses, spectacles, mirrors, windows, light-bulbs, test-tubes, windscreens. . . glass is used to make all sorts of things.

Don't drop it! You know how easily glass breaks. In the Middle Ages, you didn't have to worry much about smashing a window with your ball, because until the end of the sixteenth century most windows weren't made of glass; it was too expensive. People used oiled paper or cloth instead, which made the houses very dark.

The windows of Japanese houses used to be covered with paper, which was dampened, then stretched over a wooden frame.

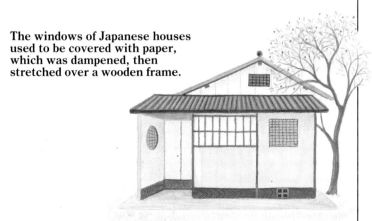

Why do we use glass in our windows?

Glass is transparent, which means it lets light through, and it also keeps out noise and cold. That's why you open your windows wide in summer, to let in the fresh air, and keep them firmly shut in winter when it's snowing outside!

Mirror, mirror, on the wall. . .

Why do you see your reflection in a mirror? The back of the glass is coated with a silver solution which reflects the light. If you hold a hand-mirror so that it catches the sunshine, you can light up a dark corner, or send a golden circle dancing around the room.

Clean and clear

Glass is very easy to clean. Lots of foodstuffs, such as jam, milk, honey and pickles, are stored in glass containers which have been sterilised first to kill off bacteria. Scientists use glass test-tubes for their experiments.

Diamonds are a glass-cutter's best friend.

Most glass can be cut with a blade made of tungsten, a very hard metal. But the most delicate glass still has to be cut with a sharp-edged diamond.

In a heated greenhouse or conservatory, plants will grow happily even when it's freezing outside.

Early glassworks were built on the edges of forests, where it was easy to gather wood to heat the furnaces.

Before it becomes hard and shiny, glass is a clear liquid.

The recipe for making glass

Traditionally, glass is made by tipping a mixture of sand, lime and soda ash into a large clay vessel, the crucible, which is then heated in a furnace to a very high temperature – 1400°C! The three ingredients fuse together to make a thick liquid, rather like extremely hot syrup, which the glass-maker can mould into different shapes. Nowadays, most glass is made in large tanks. For ten days and nights at a time, sometimes even longer, machines continuously feed in the ingredients at one end of the tank, and remove molten glass from the other.

		Sand		Lime		Soda ash
	=		+		+	

What does the glass-blower do?

First of all, he collects a blob of molten glass on the end of a hollow metal rod, the blow-pipe. Then he shapes

the glass by rolling it along the edge of a smooth table called a marver.

The glass-blower's tools: wooden mallets made of hollowed-out wood, used to shape the molten glass; scissors and tongs.

Next, he blows as hard as he can down the pipe so that the soft glass balloons up into a bulb-shape called a parison, which he can then shape on the marver into a jug or vase.

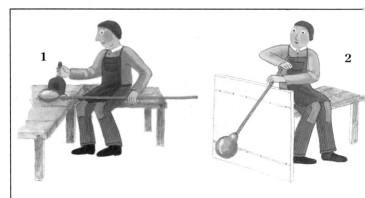

The glass-blower has to work very quickly, before the glass cools and becomes too stiff to shape.

Making a wine-glass

First, the parison is moulded to make the top of the wine-glass (1, 2). Then the glass-blower uses his scissors to cut off the left-over glass (3). He keeps just enough to make the stem, which he pulls down with his tongs (4).

This technique has hardly changed at all since Roman times.

The rim of the glass is softened with a blow-lamp before being smoothed off.

5

6

His assistant brings another blob of glass, still hot and soft. The glass-blower puts it on to the stem (5) and then shapes it in a round mould to make the foot (6). Finally, he cuts the wine-glass away from the blow-pipe, and smooths the rim carefully (7). If glass cools too quickly, it becomes brittle and shatters very easily, so the wine-glass is placed in another furnace where it is reheated and then cooled slowly (8). This proces is called annealing.

The annealing furnace is only heated to 500°C; otherwise, the glass would soften and lose its shape.

7

8

People have been making glass for over 4000 years.

Inside the Pyramids built by the Ancient Egyptians, archaeologists have discovered glass beads, cups and perfume-flasks. Some of the statues even have glass eyes. Glass was rare and expensive in Ancient Egypt; only the very rich could afford it.

Their glass didn't look much like our glass today. It was opaque, more like china, and brightly coloured, green and blue, black and white, yellow and red. Transparent glass was almost unknown until Roman times.

To make a bowl, the Egyptians first made a sand mould, then skilfully wound around it a spiral of glass paste. Once the cup had been fired, all they had to do was to shake out the sand.

The first picture-books

In the Middle Ages, hardly anyone learned to read and there were very few books; but people could read the Bible stories in the stained-glass windows of their churches. Stained glass is still made in much the same way

A few stately homes and palaces had stained-glass windows too.

as it was in medieval times. The design for the glass, the same size as the window, is traced on to a piece of card, and divided into blocks of colour. A piece of glass the right colour is cut to the shape of each different colour-block. Then the craftsman pieces them together like a jigsaw, and joins them up with strips of lead.

The craftsman's tools

Small details are painted in by hand. When the sun shines through them, the windows glisten like jewels, and the church is patterned with glowing colours.

Why do chandeliers sparkle like diamonds?

Because they are made of crystal, a special kind of glass, very pure and transparent. Lead oxide is mixed in with the other ingredients, to reflect the light; that's why crystal is so heavy. Then the crystal-maker engraves stars and flowers, lines and circles, until the crystal glitters and twinkles like a thousand tiny mirrors. Crystal is very beautiful, but very expensive.

In the centre of this pond in Portugal stands the Temple of Love, made of 1,960 pieces of crystal.

Nowadays, only special glass is made by hand. **Most of the glass we use comes from factories.**

How is a bottle made?

It is all done by machine. First, a dispenser drops a blob of molten glass into a mould. Air is puffed into the centre of the glass, to make a hollow, and to shape the neck of the bottle.

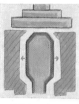

The mould opens and the bottle, still soft, is lifted into another mould, where a stronger jet of air blows it into its final shape. Then it joins the other bottles on a roller, and wobbles off to be annealed.

Don't throw your bottles away! Put them into a bottle-bank. Glass can be recycled, which saves energy and natural resources.

Until the 1960s, window glass was made by pulling a sheet of glass upwards out of a big trough of molten glass. But this method produced rough glass which had to be ground and polished to make it smooth enough for windows.

Float glass

Nowadays, window glass is made by floating the molten glass in a bath full of liquid tin. The metal is shiny and smooth, so it forms a perfect sheet of glass which doesn't need grinding or polishing; after annealing, it is ready to be cut up and sold. The whole process is done by machine, and controlled by a computer.

24

Not all glass is fragile.

Glass can be used in all sorts of unlikely places now, because people have invented ways of making it very strong. In some buildings, like airports, for example, whole walls are made of glass. Shops, banks and post-offices use burglar-proof glass. Car windows stay in one piece if a stone hits them. **How can glass be made this strong?** There are three main types of safety glass. **Wired glass** is made by pressing a netting of iron wire into the soft glass. **Laminated glass** has a layer of plastic sandwiched between two sheets of glass. **Toughened glass,** strongest of all, is made in the normal way, reheated, then cooled very quickly by blasts of cold air.

Heat-resistant cookware made of glass-ceramics

Safety glass has hundreds of uses:

from a baby's cup...

... to a porch roof.

Reflecting the city

Perhaps there are tall office-blocks in your town with walls like enormous mirrors, reflecting the street and the sky. A wall of clear glass would let everyone peer in at the people working inside, and would also make the building very hot on sunny days; so a thin metallic film is applied to the back of the glass. Gold makes the windows look bronze, nickel gives a lovely blue effect. People going past can see the whole town mirrored in the glass. And the people inside the building can watch everything that happens in the street without being seen themselves. It's rather a big job for the window-cleaners, though!

Glass-makers used to carry their glass through the streets, waiting for someone to ask them to repair a window

27

Magnifying-glass

Do you wear glasses?

Lots of people need glasses to read, or to see things in the distance. Or perhaps you have used binoculars to watch birds, or examined the tiny details of a stamp through a magnifying-glass. The special glass used for lenses is called optical glass. It is used in microscopes, too, so that scientists can study the tiniest bacteria, and in the enormous telescopes astronomers look through to see distant stars.

Telescope

Optical glass contains special chemicals. It has to be very pure, and ground and polished with great care.

Binoculars

Fire from the sun

People have found a way of using the sun's heat to provide electricity. The sun's rays are reflected on to an enormous mirror, which becomes as hot as a furnace, and the heat is used to generate electricity. You might have seen houses with special glass panels on their roofs for solar heating; the sunshine on the glass heats water for washing and central heating.

Fibre-optics

If you put a bundle of glass fibres in a casing, and shine a light on one end, the light will travel right along the fibres to the other end, because it can't escape through the casing. This is called fibre-optics. Television pictures are transmitted thousands of kilometres along fibre-optic bundles. Doctors use fibre-optic instruments during operations.

Fibre-optic bundles (1) have replaced the old system of transmitting television pictures by cable (2).

Fibre-glass insulation is made from short fibres matted together to make a kind of wool, used to wrap round hot-water tanks, or to protect houses from the winter cold.

A magic mixture

Glass fibres can also be mixed with plastic. This type of fibre-glass can be soft like cloth, or hard like wood, depending on the mixture. Because it is light, strong and fire-proof, it is used to make all sorts of things: tennis-rackets, fishing-rods, sails, skate-boards, helicopter-blades, car bumpers. . . To make fibre-glass textiles, molten glass

is squeezed out through thousands of tiny holes in the bottom of a tank. It comes out in fine threads, which are collected and wound on to bobbins.

Would you like to play marbles?

Did you know that the Ancient Egyptians used to play marbles, about 4000 years ago?

Draw a big circle on the ground, with a smaller circle in the middle: the sun. The players stand at the edge of the big circle.

Each player tries to roll a marble into the sun-circle. If you miss, you lose a turn; if you succeed, you take a step forward.

The first person to reach the sun-circle is the winner.

Index